Taking Flight
An Ever Upward™ Coloring Journal

written by Justine Brooks Froelker
illustrated by J.K. Richards

Dedication

To all of my clients and my readers,
thank you for trusting me with your stories, strengths and struggles,
and most of all for your bright shining lights.

May you fight for, take flight and soar ever upward always.

This is the story of the ever changing, yet always surviving monarch butterfly.

In other words, this is also your story.

The journey of the monarch is our journey.

The butterfly metaphor of complete metamorphosis will mean more to you when you fully understand the miracle of the entire monarch life cycle.

The miracle that, without a doubt, I believe was created to remind us of our unending change and growth throughout our own life.

Let us start from the very beginning…

What is the beginning of your story?

_____

_____

_____

_____

_____

_____

_____

_____

_____

_____

_____

_____

What are some of the most influential stories you've been told about the beginning of your life?

_____

_____

_____

_____

_____

_____

_____

_____

_____

_____

_____

_____

_____

_____

_____

_____

_____

_____

How have they made you who you are today?

The beginning of the monarch's story is the tiniest of beginnings. A female monarch will lay a total of 300 to 500 eggs. She only lays her eggs on milkweed plants, which due to urban development and the use of pesticides are greatly scarce.

The egg is a tiny white dot concealed on the underside of the milkweed leaf, when examined closely it comes to a slight point and is full of sparkling facets like a diamond.

Around day four the egg becomes translucent as we can begin to see the dark head of the monarch larvae.

Soon, just 3 to 5 days after being laid, a tiny microscopic monarch larvae will hatch.

Looking back on your life what are those early defining moments that stick out in your mind? The defining moments you think are most significant in who you are becoming today or in who you want to be.

_____

_____

_____

_____

_____

_____

_____

_____

_____

_____

_____

_____

_____

_____

_____

_____

_____

_____

_____

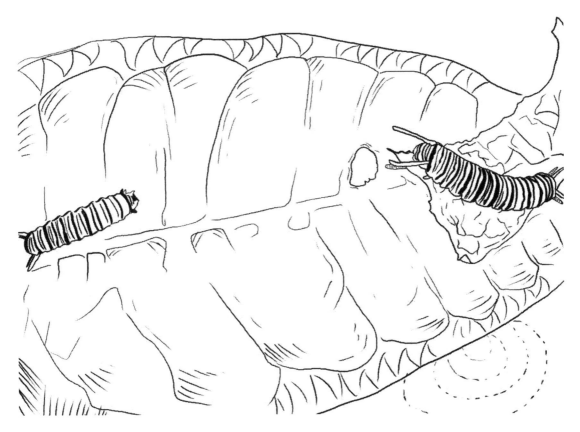

For the next two weeks the tiny larvae will grow by eating more milkweed than you can imagine.

It is also during these two weeks that the larvae will eat and poop and eat and poop and then eat some more. She will then begin to rest in order to start the growing (molting) process.

The caterpillar will appear to be resting while at the same time spinning a silk bed with her mouth in preparation of shedding her old skin to grow.

Was there a time of great change coming in your life where you had to rest but also prepare?

_____

_____

_____

_____

_____

_____

_____

_____

_____

_____

_____

_____

_____

_____

_____

_____

_____

_____

How did you practice that rest and care?

_____

_____

_____

_____

_____

_____

_____

_____

_____

_____

_____

_____

_____

_____

_____

_____

_____

_____

Soon the caterpillar will literally walk out of her old skin. She will appear a bit paler, especially around her face and her antenna will appear droopy for a while.

Do you remember a time when you had to shed your old skin to allow yourself to grow?

_____

_____

_____

_____

_____

_____

_____

_____

_____

_____

_____

_____

_____

_____

_____

_____

_____

As she walks out of her old skin, her old feet will remain stuck to the leaf behind her.

She again will rest for a bit before many times eating her own molt and moving on to continue eating and pooping and growing.

During your time of change what did you have to leave behind?

_____

_____

_____

_____

_____

_____

_____

_____

_____

_____

_____

_____

_____

_____

_____

_____

_____

_____

As you grew, what was different about the new you?

_____

_____

_____

_____

_____

_____

_____

_____

_____

_____

_____

_____

_____

_____

_____

_____

_____

_____

When the monarch caterpillar eats her own molt it is almost as if she doesn't want much evidence of her old self, except in her new, bigger and better body. However, the old body now becomes part of her, just as our past has helped shape us into who we are today. However, it is our job to write our past into our current story to help us become the person we want to be; to make sure it is no longer all of our story and only part of our story. We have the power to rewrite our endings.

How have you done this throughout your life, your struggles and your recovery from them?

_____

_____

_____

_____

_____

_____

_____

_____

_____

_____

_____

_____

_____

_____

_____

She will molt four times, literally walking out of her old skin to grow, until she is a nice and juicy 5th instar (final stage) caterpillar.

When were other times throughout your life when you had to leave the past behind in order to become a healthier and happier version of yourself?

_____

_____

_____

_____

_____

_____

_____

_____

_____

_____

_____

_____

_____

_____

_____

After about two weeks of eating and growing it is time for the caterpillar to pupate which is her total transformation, her metamorphosis.

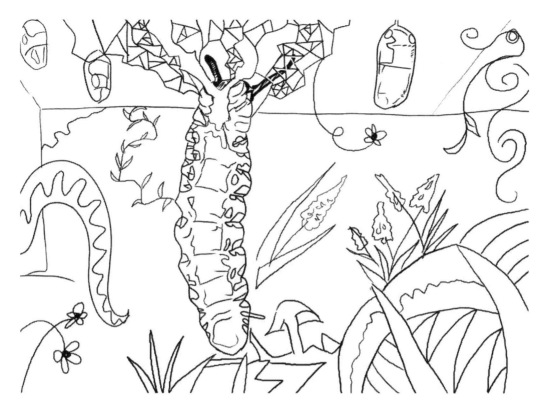

She will work hard on spinning a silk pad with her mouth. After a rest she will turn her body around to attach her prolegs (rear legs) to the silk pad she spent a day spinning.

Very slowly and carefully she will release each section of her body until she is hanging in a j position. Here she will rest for 12 to 24 hours preparing for the biggest change of her entire life.

Have you experienced a complete metamorphosis in your life; a time you emerged a completely different person on the other side of struggle, trauma, loss or tragedy?

_____

_____

_____

_____

_____

_____

_____

_____

_____

_____

_____

_____

_____

_____

_____

_____

What self-care did you make sure to practice to ensure your recovery was strong during this time of great change?

_____

_____

_____

_____

_____

_____

_____

_____

_____

_____

_____

_____

_____

_____

_____

_____

_____

_____

Once she is ready, her j position will loosen and soon her caterpillar skin will split right behind her head to reveal a bright green chrysalis (sometimes called a cocoon).

She will wiggle her old skin up over the new chrysalis and her cremaster (a spiny appendage) will pop out.

She has about 30 seconds to poke the cremaster into the silk pad she spun with her mouth. Once it is stuck, she begins to writhe around in order to drop her old skin and to securely fasten the hooks of the cremaster into the silk pad.

Again, she leaves her old skin, and in many ways never looks back to her old caterpillar body except in lifelong memories. What are you needing to leave behind? What needs to become a memory, a piece to the puzzle of your life, rather than the whole puzzle?

Over the next hour her chrysalis will harden into a beautiful jade color with shiny gold flecks.

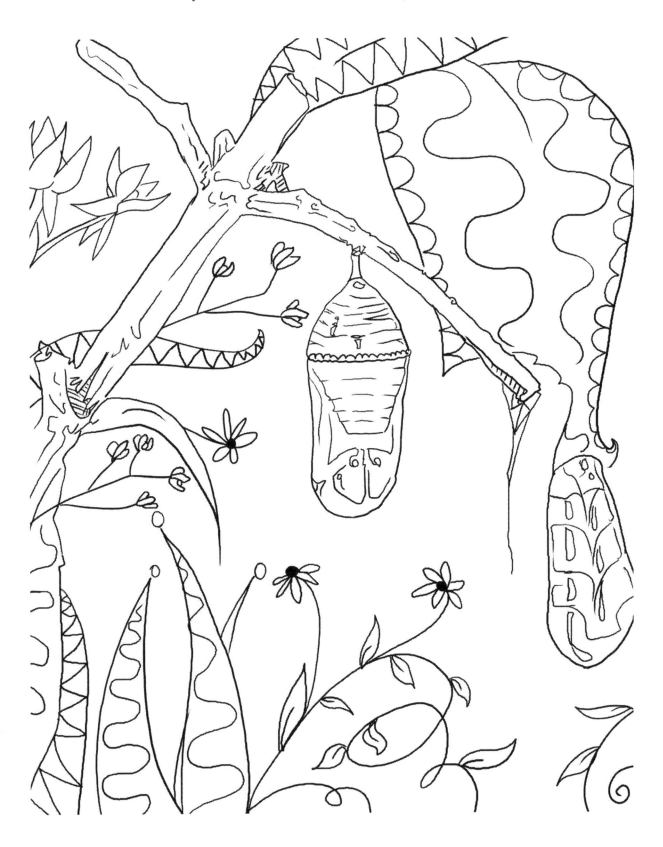

It is said the gold is for camouflage and perhaps to reflect harmful light rays from reaching the developing butterfly inside. New research shows that the gold also allows oxygen into the chrysalis for the butterfly's development; her gold is more priceless than the beauty it provides.

Sometimes the caterpillar pupates on something that is not the best for the fragile butterfly that newly emerges from the chrysalis. But her caretakers can carefully move the chrysalis to a safe place by using dental floss to tie the chrysalis to a firm foundation.

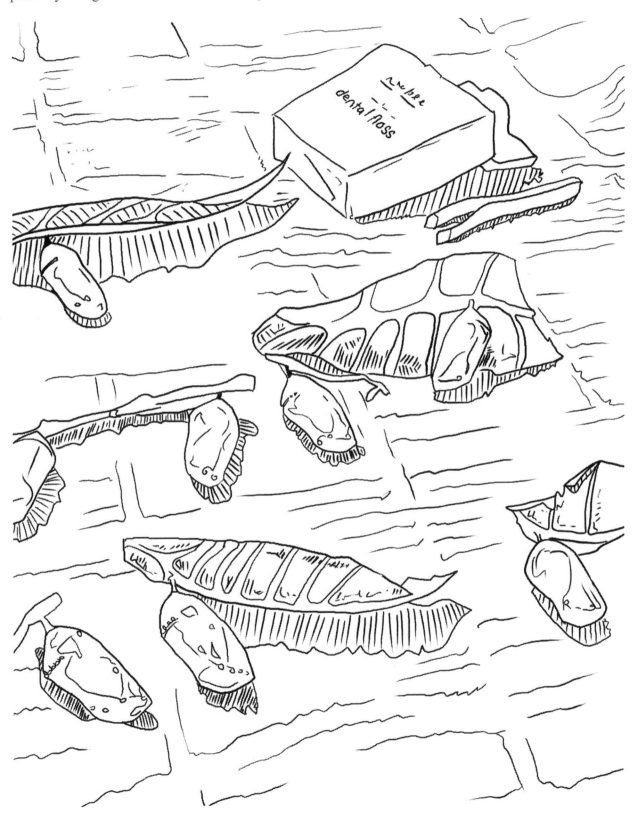

When was a time you reached out for help during your struggle? Or are you still determined to do it all yourself? This life is too hard to do it all alone. Who can you reach out to for help along the way? Who can be your firm foundation for this time of great change?

Inside the chrysalis the caterpillar becomes completely undone. Her body breaks down into a liquid of imaginal cells. Imaginal cells are much like stem cells, in the next 3-4 days these cells will grow rapidly and eventually develop into her wings, body, organs and legs.

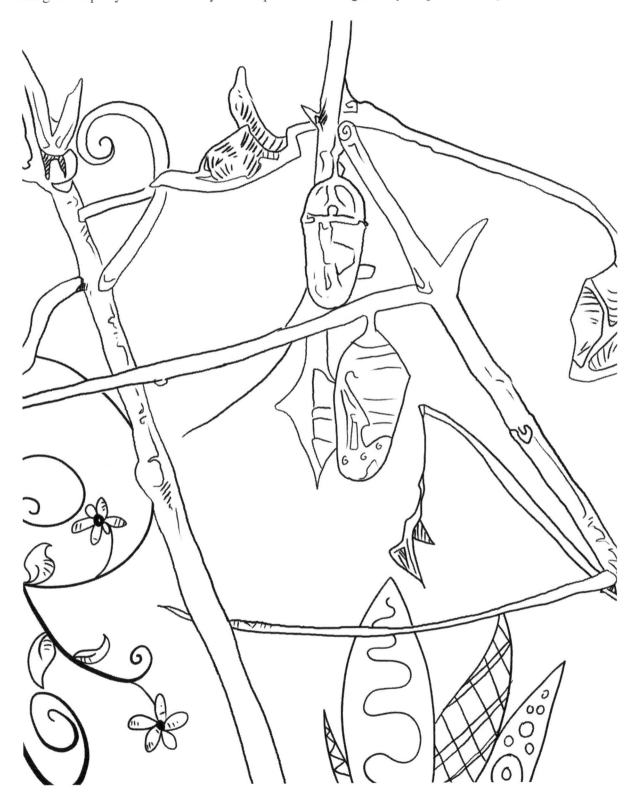

She resembles nothing of her old self and yet contains all she needs to become who she will eventually emerge, a beautiful butterfly.

This is also our journey in life. There will be times we will also feel as if we are being completely undone; undone by our losses, traumas or struggles, where our own transformation simply cannot be stopped.

What we must realize is that we have much of what we need to, not only survive through the struggle, but to also thrive on the other side of it; just as the monarch.

We simply must embrace it.

After about 10 days, the chrysalis will begin to appear dark in color as it becomes translucent and the monarch wings will become visible through it; showing evidence of the great metamorphosis that has been taking place.

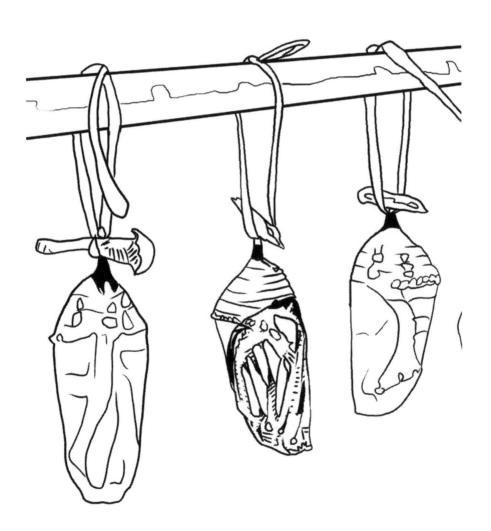

Soon it will be completely transparent, turning into a brilliant display of the undeniable orange and black of the monarch butterfly.

What has been your greatest struggle, the greatest battle and change in your life? What was your great change; your own metamorphosis like the monarch's?

_____

_____

_____

_____

_____

_____

_____

_____

_____

_____

_____

_____

_____

_____

_____

_____

_____

_____

_____

What did you create within yourself during that time? Can you now realize you have much of this power within yourself to be who you want to be; the happier, healthier and more engaged best version of yourself? Like the monarch, we already have most of what we need to emerge beautiful, we simply need to choose the new perspective.

_____

_____

_____

_____

_____

_____

_____

_____

_____

_____

_____

_____

_____

_____

_____

_____

_____

Or are you needing to create that change now? What great change, or metamorphosis, do you need to walk in to and allow to happen?

_____

_____

_____

_____

_____

_____

_____

_____

_____

_____

_____

_____

_____

_____

_____

_____

_____

_____

Was there a time in your life, during great change, where you couldn't hide the internal changes from the outside world any longer? Your new greatness, your light, was shining too bright to hide any more.

_____

_____

_____

_____

_____

_____

_____

_____

_____

_____

_____

_____

_____

_____

_____

_____

_____

And then she will emerge, her new light too much to be contained any longer.

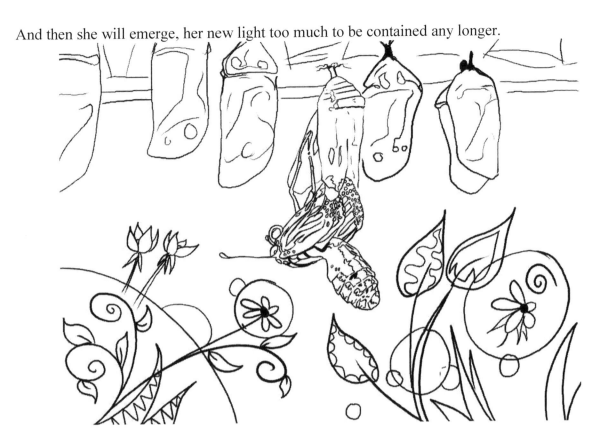

Looking nothing like the bright yellow and black striped caterpillar who created her own chrysalis and nothing like she will when she is ready to fly, the monarch butterfly emerges with tiny, wrinkled wings and a plump body.

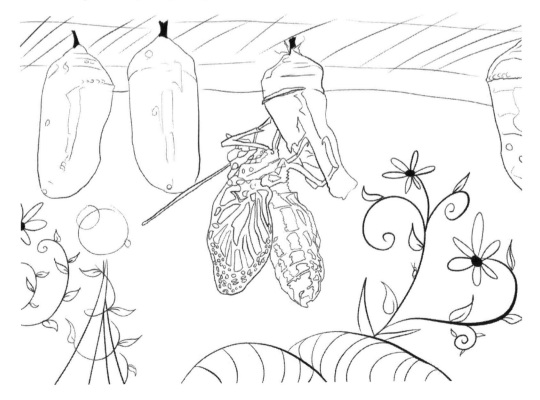

When she first emerges her proboscis is in two pieces. She must knit them together into the canal she will drink nectar through to feed.

She will then pump blood from her body into her wings, slowly inflating them to full size. She fills up her own wings with the love and strength she already has inside of herself.

Within you too is all the strength you need to prepare for your flight; including your past growth, your past mistakes and the complete change you have endured. They are part of your story.

Can you believe in this strength? What parts of you and of who you want to be will help you fill up your wings; the wings that will make you fly?

_____

_____

_____

_____

_____

_____

_____

_____

_____

_____

_____

_____

_____

_____

_____

_____

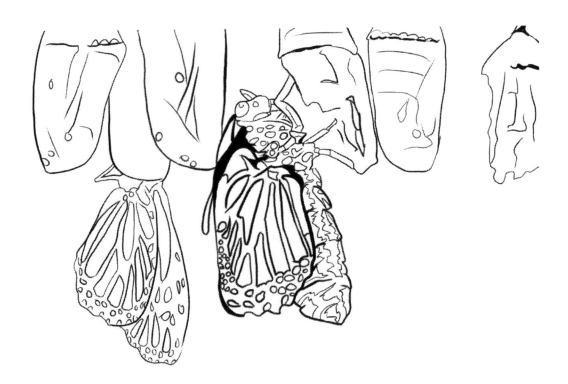

For the next four hours or so she will fill her wings, hanging upside down to allow them to dry and harden in preparation for her first flight.

When was a time you had to allow yourself time to strengthen up for the journey in front of you? How did you harness your strength?

_____

_____

_____

_____

_____

_____

_____

_____

_____

_____

_____

_____

_____

_____

_____

_____

_____

_____

_____

Soon she will begin pumping her wings as if testing them before she takes her first flight.

Have you had the test run? How did it go? Do you need to prepare for it now? What can you do? What needs to be your best next step? Or do you need more time to prepare?

Within just a few minutes of pumping her wings she is ready for her first flight. The flight to her new life, where she will feed on bright colored flowers and brilliantly shine her majestic orange wings all the way from Canada to Mexico.

On this flight she will be noticed as the beautiful monarch.

Known for her struggles to become who she is now, and known for her strength of the extraordinary migration ahead of her.

Nothing like the struggling caterpillar, and yet without her past, her beauty could not light up the world.

Who is this new version of you; this happier, healthier and bright orange winged version of you?

_____

_____

_____

_____

_____

_____

_____

_____

_____

_____

_____

_____

_____

_____

_____

_____

_____

_____

How can you make sure to have your past shine through the transformed and beautiful light you are now; to honor and embrace all the parts of your story?

_____

_____

_____

_____

_____

_____

_____

_____

_____

_____

_____

_____

_____

_____

_____

_____

_____

_____

_____

The world will forever be changed, by not only her beauty, but also by her struggle to become.

Because there was no one like her ever before nor will there ever be…just like you.

Draw or create your own *Taking Flight* artwork. Snap a photo and upload to social media using #MyTakingFlight.

For inspiration make sure to follow Justine on Facebook, Instagram and YouTube.

Journaling Notes

Made in the USA
Middletown, DE
13 May 2017